To: ....

....

From: ....

....

Date: ....

....

....

....

....

....

....

....

....

....

This edition is
published and distributed
exclusively by
DISCOVERY TOYS
Martinez, CA

Text ©1990 Discovery Toys
Illustrations ©1990 Doug Taylor

Printed in U.S.A. by
Ringier America

Designed by
Jerry Lambert, Laurel Lane

ISBN 0939979-48-9

GENERATIONS

MY
GRANDPARENTS'
REFLECTIONS

Written by Discovery Toys

Illustrated by Doug Taylor

*G*randmother and Grandfather,
tell me about the people
in your family.

*Did they ever tell you stories
about when they were little?*

*Are you like any of your grandparents in any way?
Do you think I am?*

*Do you have a favorite grandparent memory?
Please share it with me.*

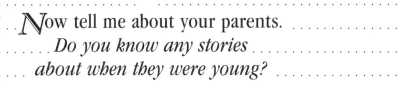

Now tell me about your parents.
*Do you know any stories
about when they were young?*

Do you know how they met each other?

*How many wedding anniversaries
did they celebrate together?*

Can you tell me something special
you remember about each of your parents?

Who do you resemble the most?

Do I resemble either of your parents?

Grandmother and Grandfather,
I wish I'd known you when you were little.

What were you like then? Do you have any photos?

What's your earliest memory?

*Tell me about the other children
in your family and
how you got along with them.*

What did your family like to do together?

*What other relatives or family friends
have been important to you?
Can you tell me their names and why they're special?*

*Are any of our relatives known
for doing something unusual?*

*D*o you remember a favorite family recipe?

Who is the oldest relative you ever met?
Did they tell you any
interesting stories about our family?

Did you ever get into trouble
for doing something you weren't supposed to?
What was it? How old were you?

What was one of your greatest adventures
when you were small? Tell me about it.

What's one of the funniest things
that ever happened to you when you were young?

What were your dreams for the future
when you were a teenager?

*Did you have a "crush" on anyone in high school?
What did you like about that person?*

*Who were your best friends
when you were growing up?
What did you do together?*

Crandmother and Grandfather,
tell me about your life together.

How did you meet?

How old were you?

What were you doing at the time?

*W*hen did you first know you wanted to marry? . . . .

Were you engaged? How long?

What was your wedding like?
Did you go someplace special
on a honeymoon?

What surprised you the most
about your new spouse after you were married?

I wonder what your first years together were like.

How many children did you want?

*T*ell me the story of my parent's birth.

*What did you think
the day my parent was born?*

How did you choose my parent's name?

*Did my parent remind you
of anyone else in your family?*

What was my parent like as a child?

What's one of the most mischievous things
my parent ever did?

What about my parent
made you especially proud?

*T*ell me about your children when they were young.

What kinds of things did you all like to do together?

What makes our family special?

As a teenager, what did my parent do
that worried you the most?

What's the funniest thing my parent ever did?

Can you tell me your favorite story
about being my parent's parent?

*Did my parent have any special interests
or achievements as a teenager?*

*When it was time for my parent
to move out and leave home,
how did you feel?*

When did you first meet my parent's spouse?
How did you feel when they decided to marry?

What was their wedding like?
Do you have a favorite memory of their wedding day?

Now, tell me what you thought
when you first saw me!

P
H
O
T
O
G
R
A
P
H
S

MEMO

RABILIA

Grandmother and Grandfather,
I wish you'd both tell me
about places important to you.

What countries did your families
originally come from?

Do you know why and when
they moved here?

Did they bring any traditions
with them?

Where and when were you born?

*Where did you live when you
were growing up?*

*Tell me about the family home
you remember most.*

What was your room like? Did you have to share it?

*Did you have a special place you liked to go
when you were a child?*

Was there any place that was scary?

Where did you go to school?

(Elementary School)

(High School)

(Other)

Did you like school?

Which subject was your favorite?

What school activities did you enjoy?

*D*id you have a part-time job?
Where? How much money did you make?

Where did you spend holidays and other vacations?

What kinds of entertainment did you enjoy?

Where did you move when you left your family's home?

How old were you then?

Where was your first full-time job?

What did you do?

Where else have you worked?

Where was your first home after you married?
What was it like?

Did you raise your family there?

*T*ell me about the places you've visited.

If you could go someplace you haven't been,
where would it be and why?

Where is your favorite place of all and why?

Where were you when I was born?

GRAPHS

M
E
M
O
R
A
B
I
L
I
A

*G*randmother and Grandfather,
please tell me about things
when you were young.

Did you have a favorite toy?

Do you remember an outfit you really loved?

*What was the very best present
you ever received?*

*What's the most memorable gift
you ever gave?*

Do you remember when you got your first skates or bicycle?
How did you learn to get around
on your new "wheels"?

How old were you
when you learned to drive a car?

What kind of car was it?

Who taught you?

What was the first car you owned?

Do you remember how much it cost?

*T*ell me about any "fads" you can remember
during your teen years.

Now tell me about your all-time favorite

book

movie star

music

singer

food

(other)

*T*ell me some things I take for granted
that were invented in your lifetime.

What was life like without them?

What year was it when you were 21?

I wonder what some of these things cost:
   soda pop   *bread*   *stamps*
   bus rides   *comic books*   *movies*
   candy bars   *gasoline*   *nice house?*

*Do you have something
that belonged to your grandparents?*

P

H

O

T

O

G

R

A

P

H

S

M EMO

RABILIA

*G*randmother and Grandfather,
could you tell me about
the interesting times of your life?

*I wonder what was happening in the world
the year you were born.*

*When you were a child or teenager,
what world events were taking place?*

Was there a time that you remember
being especially fun or significant?

What were the major news stories
when you were starting a family of your own?

Which political figure do you remember most and why?

*Can you remember a time
or an event that changed your life?*

*T*ell me about special times in our family.

Do we have a traditional way to celebrate holidays?

*H*ave we ever had a family reunion?
Where was it held? Who was there? Do you have photos?

PHOTOGRAPHS

What family weddings do you remember most?

*What other memorable occasions have taken place
in our family? Do you have photos?*

PHOTOGRAPHS

*H*ow has life changed
since your grandparents' time?

*How do you think times have changed
between your childhood and mine?*

What do you hope the future brings for me?

GRAPHS

P
H
O
T
O
G
R
A
P
H
S

$\mathcal{M}$ E M O

RABILIA

$\mathcal{M}$
E
M
O
R
A
B
I
L
I
A